SMALL & DECORATIVE FURNITURE

SMALL & DECORATIVE FURNITURE

JOHN BLY

BBC BOOKS

A MARSHALL EDITION

Published by BBC Books, a division of BBC Enterprises Ltd,
Woodlands, 80 Wood Lane, London W12 0TT

Conceived, edited and designed by
Marshall Editions
170 Piccadilly, London W1V 9DD

ISBN 0 563 37129 3

10 9 8 7 6 5 4 3 2 1

EDITORS GWEN RIGBY, HEATHER MAGRILL
ART EDITOR HELEN SPENCER
PICTURE EDITOR ELIZABETH LOVING
ASSISTANT EDITOR SIMON BEECROFT
ART DIRECTOR JOHN BIGG

ILLUSTRATIONS by János Márffy,
Stan North, Coral Mula
ALL PHOTOGRAPHS by Clive Corless,
except the following:
CHRISTIE'S IMAGES: 46; 48*c*; 63; 67*r*
COURTESY, WINTERTHUR MUSEUM: 48*b*.
r = right, *b* = bottom, *c* = centre

Valuation is an imprecise art and prices vary for
many reasons. The valuations given are estimated
auction prices at the time of going to press.
As auctions take place in the public arena, this
is considered to be the fairest value.

Origination by Master Image, Singapore
Type film by Dorchester Typesetting
Printed and bound in Portugal by Printer Portuguesa

CONTENTS

INTRODUCTION

THIS LITTLE VOLUME IS AIMED SPECIFICALLY at the collector of small and decorative furniture – larger than treen, but by no means architectural pieces. In fact, the sort of antique furniture you can put in the back of your car. It may be small but it is certainly not insignificant, for each piece reflects a period from our past as accurately as a painting or photograph. Each different timber and new design represents a development in our social history. For example, you will not find an Elizabeth I period tea caddy made of satinwood because we knew nothing of tea at that time, and satinwood had not yet been discovered. Take the dumb waiter, the davenport and the whatnot: each of these was designed to fulfil a specific need which had not existed before. It is the purpose, as well as the design and timber, that enables us to date a piece of furniture.

This is history; it is fun; and it makes the subject irresistible. Most of the small furniture brought in to the Antiques Roadshow dates from the second half of the 19th century. It was during this time that machine production revolutionized the furniture industry, enabling makers to include exotic veneers, luscious upholstery and fancy metal mounts cheaply and en masse.

Boxes and caskets are the most popular items, while small tables and chairs of every type come a close second and third. Perhaps the most common box is the travelling writing box, which opens to form a sloping lap desk. These are usually veneered with walnut or rosewood and

have a central brass plaque on the top for the owner's initials. Although military in appearance, most of these boxes were intended for the home civilian market. Since they are so common, they tend not to have great value, unless exceptional in every way; but this means they can be an ideal and inexpensive start for a collection.

Alternatively, small tables made after the 1780s can be modestly priced. Since they tended to follow the prevailing fashion, much can be learned from their design. Pairs of such tables are very rare and will fetch astronomically more than equivalent singles.

Much the same can be said for dining chairs – once again, singles are much cheaper than sets. I always recommend starting a collection with individual fine examples to create a harlequin set; each one is a conversation piece, while several will instantly add atmosphere to a dining room. A genuine, but not too grand, Chippendale period dining chair can be bought for less than £200, whereas a set of eight, all matching, can cost £10,000.

The subject of value always creates some confusion, especially when experts use different terms, such as "worth", "cost" or "insurance". The difference between these may be best explained by alluding to auctioneers who, to finance their operations, charge the vendor and the purchaser a commission. There is, therefore, a significant difference between what you get for something when you sell it – its "worth" – and what you pay for a piece when you buy it – its "cost". "Insurance" is a valuer's opinion of a future replacement cost.

John Bly.

WOODS & CONSTRUCTION

It is not always easy to identify the wood used for a piece of furniture because, although only a few types of timber were used, there has long been a tradition of making cheaper woods look like more expensive varieties.

Examine parts where the natural, unfinished wood is visible, but remember that parts not normally seen are often made from different woods from the rest of the piece. Sides of drawers, for instance, may be oak or pine, whatever timber is used elsewhere.

Strong, long-lasting native oak was used for the earliest English furniture: solidly made chests, chairs and tables. In the 1600s, oak began to be displaced by the more fashionable walnut. The most attractive pieces of wood – the burrs and curls – were taken from the weakest part of the tree and so were used mainly for veneers.

Mahogany came into wide use in the mid-1700s, when import taxes were reduced and after many walnut trees had been killed by frost.

FURNITURE WOODS

1 Oak: strong-grained wood that can vary from warm pale brown to almost black depending on the age and finish.

2 Beech: although plentiful and easy to work, it can warp.

3 Maple: less common pale wood, its "bird's eye" ringed grain was popular for veneers.

4 Walnut: faint grain with darker veining. Outgrowths produce popular burr veneers.

5 Rosewood: dark reddish-brown streaky wood used as a high-quality veneer.

6 Mahogany: rich copper-red wood which is usually stained rather darker.

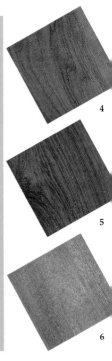

FURNITURE PERIODS IN GREAT BRITAIN

STYLE	PERIOD	DATE	WOOD
GOTHIC	ELIZABETHAN	1558–1603	OAK PERIOD (UP TO 1670)
	JACOBEAN	1603–25	
BAROQUE	CAROLEAN	1625–49	
	CROMWELLIAN	1649–60	
	RESTORATION	1660–89	WALNUT PERIOD (1670–1735)
	WILLIAM & MARY	1689–94	
ROCOCO	WILLIAM III	1694–1702	
	QUEEN ANNE	1702–14	
	EARLY GEORGIAN	1714–60	MAHOGANY PERIOD (1735–1770)
NEO-CLASSICAL	LATE GEORGIAN	1760–1811	LATE MAHOGANY PERIOD (1770–)
REGENCY	REGENCY	1811–30	

WOOD GRAIN PATTERN

This depends on the part of the tree from which the plank is cut and the angle of the cut. **1** Quarter-sawn board. **2** Flat-sawn board. **3** Irregular figuring made by growth pattern of branches. **4** "Y" pattern at junction of main trunk and branches. **5** Veneers often cut from outgrowths.

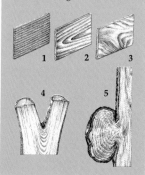

VENEERS & INLAYS

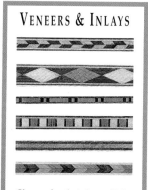

Chosen for their beautiful grain or figuring, veneers or thin sheets of wood were stuck to a plain wood carcass. Often different shapes and colours were assembled to form inlaid patterned bands (*above*) or floral (marquetry) or geometric (parquetry) designs.

The construction techniques and accessories used, as well as the type of wood, can help to date a piece of furniture and establish its authenticity.

Seats were made using plank construction, until, in the mid-1500s, joined construction was introduced. Early case furniture, such as the chest, was made using mortise and tenon joints held together with pegs and dowels; screws were first used in the early 1700s.

The frames, or carcasses, of case furniture were often quite crudely made of cheaper woods, such as pine, covered with a veneer. The backs of early pieces were not highly finished and

may be composed of three or four boards secured with irregularly shaped nails; after c.1750 more care was taken and the backs were sometimes panelled.

Mouldings, styles of legs and feet, types of handles and methods of construction of drawers all give clues to the date of a piece of furniture. But it is wise to check that handles and feet have not been replaced with changing fashions and that table tops and legs belong together.

▷ DATING WOOD SCREWS *The handmade screw (1720–1830s) (left) has an uncentred drive slot, a filed top and uneven thread. The machine-made screw (mid-1800s) has a precisely centred drive slot, a lathe-finished top and milled thread.*

DOVETAIL JOINTS & MOULDINGS

Large handmade dovetail joints (1), secured with handmade nails, were usually present on the front edges of drawers until c.1700. In the early 1700s, the number of dovetails grew and they became more regular and equal in size (2).

Mouldings overhung the drawer (3) from 1725 to 1775, and until the 1760s they were sometimes part of the drawer front (4). After 1720, this style was used together with the cockbead.

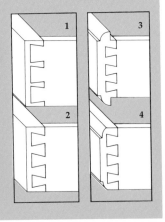

HANDLES

Shapes of handles were in keeping with the design of furniture, but many original handles have been replaced as a popular way of updating pieces. Early handles were of iron; later, steel was used, then brass, with the best quality ones gilded. From 1850 a wide variety of machine-made metal mounts appeared.

The dates given are only a guide as to when the handle type first appeared. **1** Iron drop handle, early 17th C. **2–4** Brass pendant handles, early 18th C. **5** Cast brass loop handle with engraved back plate, early 18th C. **6, 7** Cast brass loop handles, early 18th C. **8–11** Cast brass loop handles c.1750–1800; with pierced backplate (**8**); in French style with roses (**9**); decoratively cast with roses (**10**); swan neck (**11**). **12** Loop handle with stamped sheet-brass backplate, late 18th C. **13** Stamped brass knob, late 18th C. **14, 15** Cast drop handles, 1750–75; 1775–1800. **16** Regency star knob. **17–19** Victorian turned wooden knobs, often with ivory or mother-of-pearl inlay.

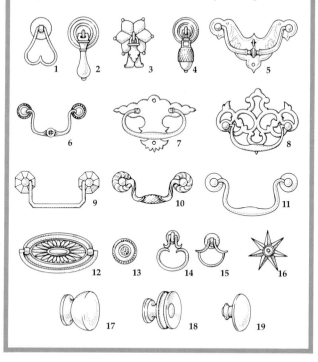

CHAIRS

In the Middle Ages, stools or benches
were the ubiquitous form of seating,
with chairs regarded as symbols of rank
and position; it was not until the 1500s that
chairs became more common.

The back stool – literally a stool with a
half back, which was far more portable than
earlier chairs – evolved in the early 1600s.

The great diversity now evident in
English chairs stems from the continental
ideas that reached the country after
the restoration of Charles II in 1660 and that
were spread by the Huguenot craftsmen
who flooded in some 25 years later.

By the 18th century, English chairs
had developed their own strong stylistic
trends, emphasized as the century
progressed by great designers such as
Chippendale, Sheraton and Hepplewhite.

With the introduction of machine-made
chairs during the 1800s, styles became more
eclectic and universal, until "reformers"
of the Arts and Crafts and Aesthetic
movements rebelled against mass
production and attempted to achieve
a purer style of hand-crafted chair.

DINING CHAIRS

By the early 18th century, English dining chairs had developed their own strong characteristics. They were made of walnut, had bold curved lines and a solid back splat and relied on the colour and pattern of the wood for decoration.

As the century progressed, the use of mahogany increased, and the simple lines of earlier chairs were embellished with carvings of shells and acanthus on crests, splats and knees.

The main designers were Chippendale, with his Rococo, Gothic and Chinese styles, and later Hepplewhite and Sheraton.

△ **WALNUT CHAIR**, *showing typical Queen Anne-style solid splat and turned back legs, combined with an outswept Chippendale-style back rail. 1710. Set of six* **£10,000**

▽ **CHIPPENDALE-STYLE CARVER**
A heavily restored mahogany chair with shell carving on the knee, which suggests that it may be Irish; one of a set of 10. 1750–60. **£800–£1,000;** *in good condition* **£3,500–£4,000**

18TH-CENTURY CHAIR STYLES

In the early 1700s, chairs were bold and curved, with little carving and solid splats. Carving increased over time, and by the 1750s splats were elaborately pierced and legs were straight or cabriole shaped. The fashionable styles ranged from Classical through Gothic and Rococo to chinoiserie.

1720–25

1750–55

◁ **MAHOGANY ARMCHAIR**
This Chippendale-style armchair, with delicately carved pierced, interlaced splat and crested rail in Gothic style are typical of mid-18th century designs. 1760–65; 3ft high. **£800–£1,200**

▽ **HEPPLEWHITE-STYLE CHAIR**
made in mahogany, with a Classical shield back in the wheatear design. It is one of a set of six which still have their original covering of green hide. Early 1800s. **The set £3,500**

△ **LADDERBACK ARMCHAIR** *with double-curved horizontal splats and curved seat; one of a pair. 1770; 3ft 4in high.* **The pair £4,500**

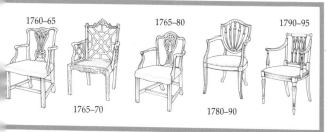

1760–65   1765–80   1790–95

1765–70   1780–90

Chair styles were very varied in the 19th century. The Neo-classical styles of the late 1700s were still strong in the early years, but they were less delicate than those of Hepplewhite and Sheraton.

Regency dining chairs, with their curved top rails, sabre legs and reeded frames, were elegant. Carving was restrained, with motifs usually derived from Greek architecture and limited to the top rail and splat. In the late Regency and William IV periods, chairs had over-hanging top rails and straight legs. Then, over the next 20 years, a new form evolved in which the top rail merged with the upright supports to make a curved oval shape – the balloon back, at its height in 1850–70.

Later design was a hotch-potch of influences, among them Gothic, Elizabethan and Rococo, and those of "reformers" such as the Arts and Crafts Movement.

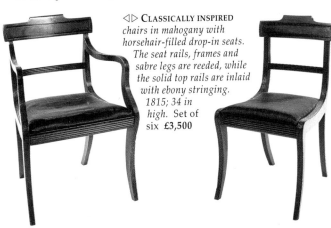

◁▷ **CLASSICALLY INSPIRED** *chairs in mahogany with horsehair-filled drop-in seats. The seat rails, frames and sabre legs are reeded, while the solid top rails are inlaid with ebony stringing. 1815; 34 in high. Set of six* **£3,500**

STYLES OF CHAIR BACK

Top rails were embellished with crests and shallow relief carving, while splats were usually simple or had pierced horizontal bars. Backs were also made in variations of trellis and X-shaped patterns.

OVERHANGING
TABLET RAIL

SOLID RAIL,
X-SHAPED SPLAT

SCROLLED CREST,
HORIZONTAL SPLAT

TABLET RAIL,
TRELLIS SPLAT

◁ **REGENCY DINING CHAIR** *A fine mahogany chair, one of a set comprising four side chairs and two carvers. It has an overhanging top rail, centre splats and turned, tapering legs. The seat is stuffed. 1835; 35in high.* The set **£2,500**

▷ **MAHOGANY ARMCHAIR** *that revives the Classical style popular 100 years earlier. The tapering legs with outswept feet and the cross bars below the X-framed splats are turned, and both top rail and seat rail are decorated with painted festoons. Late 1800s; 34in high.* **£500–£700**

◁▷ **BALLOON-BACK CHAIRS** *The deeply curved back and legs of the rosewood chair (left) are typical of the French Revival movement. 1860; 3ft high.* **£150**
Balloon-back chairs with deep upper rails (right, one of a pair) became highly popular in the late 19th C. 1875; 3ft high. The pair **£300**

HALL & SIDE CHAIRS

From the reign of George II, chairs were placed along the entrance halls and corridors of large houses where people sat and chatted or visitors waited. These hall chairs, made originally of mahogany and later of oak, are distinguished by their solid unshaped seats. Side chairs, however, were more comfortable chairs that lined the walls of reception rooms for use when extra seating was needed.

The best hall chairs are those with architectural carving in the style of pilasters or formalized drapery. Some fine early 18th-century pieces with black or, in rarer cases, red lacquer decoration can also be found. Painted details, such as a family coat of arms or a crest, may help determine the original owner and location of a piece.

Sets of hall chairs are often now split into pairs or groups of four. Since demand is not great for these rather less comfortable chairs, superb examples of 18th-century craftsmanship can be found at affordable prices.

▽ **ROUT SEAT** *Such chairs were used to rest on during dances, known as routs. Their seats may be damaged from years of hard use, perhaps as a prop while the owner polished or tied his boots. 1760–80; 4ft high.* Set of six £8,000

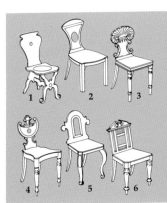

TYPES OF HALL CHAIR

Chair design reflects the style of the period in which it was made: **1** George II curvilinear chair (1745–65). **2** Mahogany chair with tapered legs (1780–1800). **3** Carved shell-back chair with turned and reeded legs (1820–60). **4** Curved-back chair. (1840–80). **5** Georgian-style carved chair with cabriole legs (1870–1910). **6** Georgian-style square-framed chair (1880–1910).

△ **MID-VICTORIAN CHAIR** *The decorative details on this solid walnut chair include cabriole legs and a lozenge-shaped back with a central panel over a pair of "C" supports. 1865; 30in high.* **£150**

△ **MAHOGANY CHAIR** *Best described as being in French Baroque style, this Victorian side chair displays a typically 19th-century melange of earlier styles. 1860s; 30in high.* **£150**

△ **CHINESE EXPORT CHAIR** *This 18th-century-style huang hua li chair is typical of the furniture mass produced in China for the European market in this period. Late 19th century; 3ft 4in high.* **£400–£500**

△ **X-FRAME CHAIR** *A mahogany and walnut chair whose design derives from the "curule" chair of the Regency period, in turn adapted from the sella curulis, or stool, of ancient Rome. 1875–80; 35in high.* **£450**

△ **CAROLEAN CHAIR** *While not strictly a hall chair because of its padded seat, this type was often used as such. The barley-sugar twist supports and pierced frame were copied in the 1800s. 17th century; 4ft high.* **£450**

△ **WALNUT CHAIR** *The Baroque style of this highly ornate chair is intriguing; the curves of the upper back are in the form of new moons, but the carving on the lower part does not match. 1850; 3ft 10in high.* **£450**

COUNTRY CHAIRS

Made from locally available woods by provincial craftsmen, country furniture has its own style and charm. Country chairs were made in a variety of woods – including beech, elm, ash and yew – and their design varied from those traditional to the region to adaptations of the most fashionable styles.

The most popular country chairs are Windsor chairs. These were originally made of beech in the area of the Chiltern Hills. It was quite common for the chairs to be assembled from parts made by several local craftsmen and then taken to Windsor to be sold, hence the name. Nowadays Windsor chair is a generic term that is used to describe a style of chair.

Country chairs can often be bought very reasonably because they tend to be found as singles rather than in sets.

◁ **FINE OAK CHAIR**
Made in the late 17th century, this chair probably belonged to a wealthy farming family. The small pegs near the top are a good indication of age. They stick out because the wood has shrunk over the centuries. 1670–1700; 3ft 6in high.
£1,800

WINDSOR CHAIRS

Chair with Gothic-arch back and splats pierced like a church window (1750–90).

Chair with swept-back arms, cabriole legs and curved crinoline-type stretcher (1770–1830).

Simple, low-backed Windsor-style chair popular from the 1830s to the present.

▷ **ROCKING CHAIR** *The rather flat turning on this chair not only indicates that it was made by a provincial craftsman but also helps with the dating. Unusually, this chair is made of yew wood rather than the more common elm or beech. Although such chairs are attractive, they have proved quite difficult to sell. Late 19th century; 4ft high.* **£1,500**

◁ **TALL-BACKED BOX CHAIR** *The cheek-shaped panels on this chair were designed to protect the sitter from draughts. It was made using the frame and panel method. 1780–90; 4ft 5in high.* **£1,250**

▷ **COUNTRY ARMCHAIR** *The curious mixture of the highly fashionable vase-shaped splat, crest rail and pad feet together with the old-style turned supports and gap between the seat and back mark this oak armchair as a provincial interpretation of the latest London style. 1700–10; 3ft 7in high.* **£550**

OCCASIONAL CHAIRS

A great variety of chairs exists aside from upholstered and dining styles. Broadly termed occasional chairs, most of these pieces were intended for a specialized activity, such as reading, while others were kept simply as spare chairs.

One early form of occasional chair, which dates from at least medieval times, is the turned type, so called because it was made by turners rather than by joiners or carpenters.

In Georgian and Regency times an unusual form of library chair with an attached bookrest was produced for use when reading or writing. Also popular at this time was the corner chair, with a leg at the front and back and two at the sides. Known in France as *fauteuils de bureau*, they were placed in the corner of a room for reading.

▷ **BEVAN CHAIR** *One of a pair of rare oak chairs designed by the architect Charles Bevan for the Leeds firm Marsh, Jones and Cribb. The chairs carried a patent and were made in a style favoured by the Arts and Crafts Movement. 1860s; 3ft 4in high.* **£5,000**

◁ **VICTORIAN REVIVAL CHAIR** *made of carved oak in what is intended to be Restoration style with a Spanish leather seat. The Victorian taste for reviving earlier furniture styles is much in evidence here. 1880; 20in wide.* **£300–£400**

△ **OAK SHIP'S CHAIRS** *Apart from the stretchers, the pair displays the Hepplewhite style and would once have been part of a larger set.*

Features that identify these as ship's chairs include brass number *plates on the back; interchangeable cane or stuffed seats; and a bolt-hole through the centre of the stretchers which allowed them to be attached to the deck. 1900; 3ft high.* **The pair £2,000**

◁ **WALNUT AND INLAID CHAIR** *Early 18th-century Dutch furniture, such as this, is attractive and often underrated. 1730; 17in wide.* **£200–£300**

▷ **WINGED ROCKING CHAIR** *with a side drawer. This is an uncommon example of a "lambing" chair since it is made of solid mahogany instead of oak, which is more usual. It may, therefore, have been made as a retirement present or a presentation piece. 1800; 3ft 4in high.* **£400–£600**

23

STUFFED CHAIRS

Fully upholstered chairs date from the late 17th century. The stuffing was mainly horsehair on a webbing base, with a wooden bar down the centre of the back and seat and a roll of horsehair along the front edge of the seat. Chairs became considerably more comfortable when, in 1828, coiled springs and then buttonback upholstery were introduced.

The materials for covering chairs changed with the new upholstery techniques. As well as leather, there was turkey work, a knotted pile fabric with patterns based on Turkish rugs.

Silks and velvet became fashionable in the 1700s; later, damask, patterned velvets and tapestry work were used. In the late 18th century brocaded satin and silks with striped or medallion patterns were common.

With the advent of mass-produced furniture in the 1800s, fabrics became cheaper.

◁ ARMCHAIR WITH ROSEWOOD FRAME *The high quality of this chair, with its scroll arms, baluster legs and serpentine-fronted seat, is indicated by the large amount of well-carved rosewood on show. 1865; 3ft high.* **£1,250**

◁ **ROSEWOOD-FRAMED SIDE CHAIR**
*Padded chairs like this one were
armless so as to accommodate
Victorian ladies' billowing skirts
and show them off. The date and
quality of this chair are evident in
the amount of rosewood around the
frame. 1835; 3ft 3in high.* **£650**

▽ **GEORGE III LIBRARY ARMCHAIR**
*Such chairs were often called
"Gainsborough" chairs since the
artist seated his models in them.
The upholstery would originally
have been leather or damask, and
brown porcelain castors have
replaced leather ones. 1700s.*
£2,500

◁ **LOUIS XV-STYLE ARMCHAIR**
*which is part of a salon suite. It
is one of many pieces made at the
turn of the 19th century when the
vogue for reviving earlier styles
was at its height. The rosewood
frame is fairly unusual: the wood
in a more expensive example
would have been gilded. 1900;
35in high.* **£1,000**

TABLES

The types and sizes of tables have, over the centuries, been governed to some extent by the other uses to which the rooms housing them have been put.

The first tables used in medieval great halls were trestle tables – large planks of wood supported on trestles – that would be cleared away after the meal so that the hall could be used for entertainments.

By Tudor times, the lord's family had begun to dine in a separate room, which resulted in the type of fixed table now known as a refectory table. As the number of smaller houses, and so demand, increased from the mid-1600s, folding tables became popular because they could be moved out of the way when not in use.

Gradually, the range of tables made for specific purposes grew to cater for an increasingly sophisticated way of life, with special tables for tea and cards among them. The list was almost endless, as was the skill and ingenuity displayed in making the tables, in the woods used and in their decoration with carving, marquetry, ormolu and gilding.

SIDE TABLES

Intended to stand against the wall, side tables have been made since the 15th century. These tables, which were used as an additional surface at mealtimes or for holding ornaments, were among the first furniture to be made.

Yet they only became fashionable in the mid-18th century, when they were included in grand sets of furniture and were used both as writing tables and dressing tables.

A typical side table from this time can be identified by the overhang top supported on a rectangular frame; the single drawer; and turned, tapering or cabriole legs. It would usually

◁ OAK SIDE TABLE
Dating from the late 17th century, this joined table with bobbin-turned legs is in exceptionally fine condition. Opening the drawer reveals fine dovetails and cleat ends (narrow strips of wood for strengthening the top) which are all signs of quality craftsmanship. 1670; 30in wide. **£4,500**

THE EVOLUTION OF THE SIDE TABLE

The first side tables were box shaped and had outside stretchers. Early 18th-century designs were more ornate before returning to Classical styling later in the century.

1 Oak table with bobbin-turned legs (1690). **2** X-stretcher table with shaped apron (1700). **3** Early Georgian table with cabriole legs (1730). **4** George III square-legged table (1760).

have been made of mahogany, although oak, elm and beech were frequently used for less sophisticated pieces.

Two new types of side table developed during the 1700s. Console tables were attached to the wall and had only two front legs, although a mirror fixed behind them gave the appearance of four. Pier tables, as the name suggests, were designed to stand in a pier, the space between two windows.

▽ **MID-GEORGIAN TABLE** *Used as a lowboy, or dressing table, this piece is of exceptional quality. It has an attractive deeply shaped apron and cabriole legs ending in pad feet. 1755; 30in wide.* **£4,500**

◁ **MAHOGANY SIDE TABLE** *from the mid-18th century with caddy-moulded overhang top. The cast brass swan-neck handle and escutcheon are typical of the period. 1750; 3ft wide.* **£2,000**

▷ **CARVED OAK SIDE TABLE** *Although this provincial table was made in the late 1700s, its most noticeable feature – the extensive carving – dates from around 1900. In this instance, the carving is quite attractive. c.1770; 28in wide.* **£800**

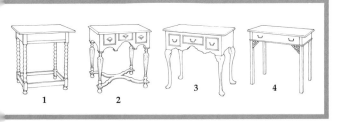

PEMBROKE & SOFA TABLES

Thomas Sheraton, the famous 18th-century designer, maintained that the Pembroke table was named after the Countess of Pembroke, since she was the first to order one.

These useful tables were generally rectangular or oval in shape with a single drawer in the centre and a hinged dropleaf on each side. They were usually kept with the leaves folded down, but were opened when needed for meals, writing or drawing.

Although first made in the late 18th century, sofa tables only became popular in the Regency period. Designed to stand in front of a sofa, they were longer than Pembroke tables, usually had drawers on both sides and were often highly decorated.

▽ **SATINWOOD PEMBROKE TABLE**
This attractive table is beautifully painted with garlands of flowers along the frieze drawer and around the outside of the unusually shaped top. The turned and tapering legs, decorated with leaf patterns, can be used to date the table since they are sturdier than those made after 1800. 1785; 32in wide. **£25,000**

LOPER JOINTS

The narrow strips of wood that fold out to support the drop-leaves of a Pembroke table are known as lopers.

They were attached to the table using wooden hinged knuckle joints secured with a wood or steel pin.

△▷ **PAINTED PEMBROKE TABLE**
In the 1780s, when it was made, this satinwood table would have been plain. The decoration of Neo-classical cherubs, flowers and festoons was added about 100 years later when painted furniture became fashionable. 1785; 4ft 2in wide. **£8,000**

△ **SOFA TABLE**
Decorated throughout with ebony stringing, this Regency rosewood sofa table rests on a tapering central pedestal and splayed legs. c.1810; 4ft 7in long (open) x 29in high. **£4,850**

OCCASIONAL TABLES

In the second half of the 18th century, society was stable and there was steady economic growth. These conditions produced a rapidly increasing group of middle-class and professional people requiring the trappings of an earlier and grander age – but accommodated in much smaller houses.

As a result, furniture was not kept in a set place but was moved around to suit the activities of the household. A circular tilt-top table, for example, would have been used as both a tea table at tea time and a supper table later in the evening. When not in use, it would have been pushed back against the wall, out of the way.

Likewise, drop-leaf tables were much in vogue because, with the flaps down, they took up little space, but provided a considerable surface area when opened up.

▷ MAHOGANY TEA TABLE
This tilt-top table started out quite plain. The ornate carving in imitation Georgian style was added to the top and legs much later. Mid-18th century; 31in wide. **£750**

◁ THIS GEORGIAN-STYLE TABLE'S *inlaid top and the painting on its curved imitation bamboo legs, which look back to Regency styles, are derived from Sheraton and Hepplewhite. c.1890.* **£1,200**

▽▷ **A fine Victorian table**
made of burr maple with gilt
metal mounts and ebony and
boxwood stringing. A band of
stringing runs around the inlay
on the legs, and the top has been
delicately inlaid with ivory in the
form of lily of the valley. c.1885;
27in high. **£3,500**

◁ **French table à volets**
with four flaps (volet is
French for shutter) which
can be raised when needed.
It is typical of a large
number of tables made of
ebonized wood, in cheap
imitation of imported
Chinese lacquer ware.
The inlay is inserted into
a panel of thuya wood
from the Atlas Mountains.
1870; 3ft 3in wide x
3ft 3in high. **£400–£600**

Tripod Tables

The tripod table was at the height of its popularity in the Georgian period (1714–1811), when designers and craftsmen such as Chippendale were producing fine mahogany pieces.

Throughout this period, the basic design did not change, although the block at the base of the column disappeared after *c*.1750 and, from time to time,

different styles of leg were used.

The main variations were in the decoration. Some table tops had plain rounded edges, some were dished and others had a carved, scalloped edge known as "pie crust". A few had turned or fretwork galleries around the edge, and on those known as supper tables the top had recesses for plates or dishes.

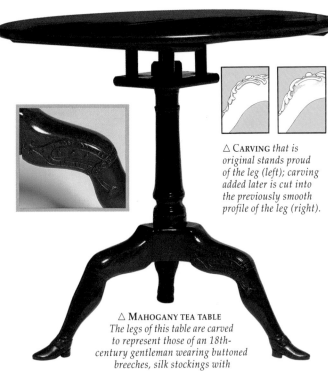

△ CARVING *that is original stands proud of the leg (left); carving added later is cut into the previously smooth profile of the leg (right).*

△ MAHOGANY TEA TABLE
The legs of this table are carved to represent those of an 18th-century gentleman wearing buttoned breeches, silk stockings with elaborately tasselled garters and buckled shoes. Such pieces were known as Manxman tables – a reference to the three-legged emblem on the flag of the Isle of Man. 1750; 28in high. **£2,500**

ANATOMY OF A TRIPOD TABLE

This simple oak table has a plain top but also some sophisticated features. It was probably made by a country craftsman who was a turner, rather than a cabinet maker, since the column is finely detailed. The legs, top and birdcage mechanism – a complex feature that allows the table to rotate as well as tilt – are, however, quite crudely made. *c.*1740; 30in high. **£7,500**

△ *The brass catch locks the top in place when the table is in use.*

△ **BIRDCAGE MECHANISM**
The main column passes through a central hole in two blocks under the table. It is held in place (while being free to rotate) by the four small columns. To enable the table to tilt, two corners of the top block extend to form lugs, which connect to runners under the table top.

△ *The claw and ball foot (left) and the pad foot (centre and right) were used between 1740 and 1770.*

TEA TABLES

The ceremony and importance attached to making and drinking tea may be difficult to understand, but in the late 1600s, when tea drinking first became fashionable, tea was expensive and highly prized.

By 1727, when George II ascended the British throne, it had become customary to entertain friends to tea at home, and a variety of tables was made to cater for this. Among them were tilt-top tables, tables with fold-over tops, the ubiquitous little tripod table to hold individual cups, urn tables, kettle tables and highly decorative teapoys.

Popular during the 1800s, when more types of tea became available, teapoys were, in effect, large tea caddies on stands. They often contained as many as four small boxes holding different teas, which were then mixed in a central glass bowl.

◁ **A FRENCH-STYLE TEAPOY** *containing two boxes for different teas and a glass bowl for sugar. It is decorated with fine figured veneers, marquetry panels and ormolu mounts. 1870; 29in high.* **£2,000–£2,500**

▷ **CIRCULAR TEAPOY** *The galleried lid of this teapoy rises on an umbrella support to reveal two tea caddies and two glass bowls. 1830–37; 4ft high.* **£2,500**

▷ **MAHOGANY TEA TABLE**
*This English tea table, with a
scalloped top edge and apron
and an under-tier, is typical of
its period. Both the top and
under-tier are inlaid with a floral
design and decorative boxwood
stringing, and there is stringing
on the shaped legs and apron also.
Early 1900s; 24in wide.* **£350**

△ **REGENCY TEA TABLE** *A fold-over
mahogany table with rosewood
crossbanding and sabre legs ending
in brass castors. The interior wood
is a bright red and the inside well
for storing table linen is still lined
with the original blue paper.
1812–30; 34in wide.* **£2,000–£2,500**

CASTORS

1 Leather castor, mid-18th
C. **2** Brass cup castor, late
18th C. **3** Brass square-
toe castor, late 18th C.
4 Brass tapered cup castor,
late 18th C. **5** Iron insert
castor with earthenware
wheel, 19th C. **6** Lion's-
paw cast brass toe castor,
early 19th C. **7** Cast brass
toe castor, early 19th C.

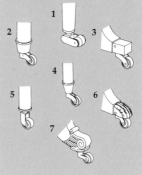

CARD TABLES

Boards for playing games such as backgammon and chequers have been in use since Tudor times. But it was only after the restoration of the English monarchy in 1660, under Charles II, that tables were made specially for games.

Most card tables were rectangular with a flap that opened up to reveal the lined playing surface. On early tables this lining tended to be velvet or needlework; baize became popular only in the early 1700s. When not in use, the flap was closed up and the table pushed against a wall.

In the Neo-classical period, semicircular card tables – the top opened to provide a circular playing area – became popular, and all tables were decorated with marquetry or crossbanding.

◁ **CONCERTINA CARD TABLE**
The fold-over top of this laburnum George II table rests on legs that extend using the concertina mechanism – a sign of quality. When open, the table is lined with green baize and has recesses for candles and money. 1730; 29in high x 35in wide. **£8,500**

Several mechanisms were designed to support the table flap. Which one was chosen for a particular table depended on when it was made and the quality of the piece.

Special tables were made for both games and cards. They usually had a well for playing backgammon and a reversible sliding top with a chess board marked on it.

Since card and games tables are decorative, compact in size and useful, they are highly sought after today.

◁ **VICTORIAN WALNUT CARD TABLE**
Decorated with highly figured walnut veneers, this fold-over card table has rather exuberant curvilinear supports. Although such flamboyance was popular in Victorian times, most card tables rested on a central pedestal. 1850; 31in high. **£3,000**

FOLDING MECHANISMS

Most card and games tables folded up so that they could stand against a wall when not in use. The quality and age of a piece determined the mechanism used. The simplest early tables had one or two hinged legs to support the flap (**1**). The more expensive concertina mechanism (**2**), introduced in the 1700s, had hinged sides that straightened as the back legs were pulled out. The hinge and swivel mechanism (**3**) was a sturdy 19th-century innovation.

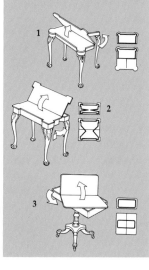

◁ **AMERICAN CARD TABLE** *When this mahogany table was made, many Europeans were migrating to America taking furniture styles with them. It is a mixture of the English Regency style with some Germanic and Rococo influence. The stencilled green baize is a rare feature. 1850s; 24in wide.* **£2,000**

WORK TABLES

Needlework accessories were, until the mid-1700s, kept in baskets or in the compartmented boxes used to hold lace. These were 12 to 14 inches long and were often covered in oyster veneer; it was a small step to mount such a box on a stand, so transforming it into a work table.

There were several variations on this basic design by the 1780s,

and the prevailing Classical style is reflected in the work tables' straight, tapering legs and elegant proportions. By the 1830s designs were even more varied, and the Victorians borrowed from many periods and styles.

Tables were lined with fine, often brightly coloured, paper and had lids lined with silk; some have a deep silk bag.

△ **ROSEWOOD WORK TABLE** *Every middle-class family would have owned a work table such as this, which is typical of its period. It is, however, of better than average quality, with drop-leaves flanking the single drawer and a silk-lined bag. 1830s; 30in high.* **£2,500**

▷ **CONICAL WORK TABLE** *Although some of the marquetry is missing, this rosewood table with a walnut base is of good quality. Such tables are prone to woodworm and, if the base has been affected, can be found mounted on blocks of wood. Late 1800s; 3ft high.* **£350**

ANGLO-INDIAN WORK TABLE

This elaborately pierced and carved table is made of rosewood. It is a versatile piece that could be used as a sewing table – note the work basket underneath – and, less obviously, as a writing desk. Inside the drawer is a rising slope on which to rest a book.

This style was popular between the 1830s and 1860s. It would have been made by a local Indian craftsman to the order of an Englishman living in India at the time of the British Raj.
20in wide. **£1,500**

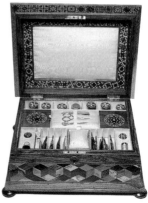

△ **ROSEWOOD SEWING BOX** *The type of inlay on this sewing box is known as parquetry – a form of marquetry based on a repeated, geometric pattern executed in woods of contrasting grain and colour. Here, the pattern on the exterior is carried through to the inside of the box and the fittings. c.1830; 14in wide.* **£1,200**

CHESTS &
CHESTS
OF DRAWERS

Typically constructed from native
and local woods, chests made of oak have
proved the most durable and, in
consequence, exist in the largest numbers
today. Collectors look for pieces that
display fine colouring and original carving,
and the survival of the original lock is an
added bonus. Chests of drawers were used
in virtually every room of the house from
the mid-17th century. As a result,
they form a large part of the antique
furniture around today, and good-quality
18th- or 19th-century examples can be
found relatively inexpensively.

Most desirable, however, are
well-proportioned, veneered pieces made
of fine quality timber in original condition.
Bombé and serpentine-shaped examples
command high prices, with smaller
chests also much sought after.

CHESTS

The earliest known type of furniture is the rectangular, top-opening coffer, or chest, and examples from ancient Egypt have been found. The earliest existing European chests, which were constructed rather than hollowed-out from logs, date from the 1200s. They are made of planks joined by nails; some of them have handles and are banded with iron for strength. By the 1500s, chests were of panelled construction, with mortise and tenon joints held by dowels.

Until the end of the 17th century, most fine chests were made of oak. In the 17th century drawers were added at the bottom of the chest, making access to stored items easier. Such hybrids were known as mule chests, and they remained popular throughout the 1700s.

Chests declined in popularity as cabinet-making techniques improved and chests of drawers became more widely available.

▷ **OAK TROUSSEAU BOX** *Such chests were used by brides for storing marriage clothes and linen. Foul-smelling candles were stored in a box inside the lid to deter moths. The carving is original and the existence of a key exceedingly rare. Early 17th century; 21in wide.* **£800–£1,200**

△ **PANELLED CHEST** *The precise and intricate, if fairly basic, chip carving displayed on this piece would have been made using a round punch and half-round chisel with the aid of a rule and compasses.*

Such designs using basic tools are typical of the time. The chest, which still has its original hinges, would probably have stood at the end of a bed for storing bed linen. 17th century; 4ft long. **£1,500**

△ **OAK BLANKET CHEST** *The original lock and hinges, and fine carving and colour, make this is a superb example of a panelled chest. With oak furniture, it can* *be difficult to differentiate between a genuine 17th-century piece and a 19th-century revival; carving was often added later. 1640; 3ft 6in long.* **£2,500**

△▷ **LARGE OAK CHEST** *with early Gothic carved front panels (right) and a superb lock plate with decorated borders. The panels are ecclesiastical in form and date from the 15th century, but the rest of the chest was made later. Oak was the standard timber for ecclesiastical fitments between the 9th and 15th centuries. 19th century; 4ft 7in long.* **£1,200**

CHESTS OF DRAWERS

From the mid-17th century, oak chests of drawers were widespread. Most examples seen today, however, date from the mid-18th century to the mid-19th century, with the majority made of mahogany.

When determining the age of a chest, a general overview can help establish its type. Bedroom furniture, for instance, is most often unadorned, while drawing room pieces are far more lavish and highly decorated.

Further information can be gleaned from the materials used, the construction, the drawer handles and the feet. Beware, however, when looking at handles, since they are easily changed. This may be indicated by indentations on the drawer front and dissimilar woods.

In England after 1660, panel and frame construction was replaced by the European method of case construction. In this method, a carcass made of inexpensive wood is veneered with high-quality wood for a more sumptuous look.

A reliable guide to age is the slide mechanism on the drawers. Early pieces have drawers which pull straight out. From the late 17th century runners were used, until c.1710, after which drawer sides were made flat again. Side runners returned to vogue in the present century.

△ LABURNUM CHEST *with superb oyster veneering. While the feet are rather clumsy replacements, the handles are replicas of the originals. 1689–95; 3ft 4in wide.* **£12,000–£15,000**

CHANGING STYLES OF CHESTS OF DRAWERS

Early examples looked like chests but were, in fact, a set of drawers with cupboard doors on the front. By the 17th century, doors had been replaced by decorated drawer fronts.

The usual style, with drawers becoming deeper from top to bottom, was established by the early 18th century; later pieces were often simply larger, with more distinctive bracket feet.

Bow fronts were popular between about 1750 and 1775, with the deepest bows found on the finest pieces. After 1770, the serpentine top was added.

△ **EARLY OAK CHEST** *The joined construction and carved drawer fronts in this fine piece are of exceptional quality. The handles and feet are replacements, but the carving could date from the reign of James I (1603–25). Early 17th century; 3ft 3in high.* **£4,000**

STYLES OF FEET AND MOULDINGS

As well as the feet and the edge moulding along the top of a piece, grain pattern is a guide to age: before 1730, it runs down the moulding; after 1740 it runs lengthways.

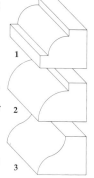

BRACKET FOOT 1720–80

BRACKET FOOT 1720–80

TURNED FOOT 1850

OGEE FOOT 1740–75

SPLAY FOOT 1780–1810

TURNED FOOT 1870

The style of moulding along the top of a chest can indicate its age.

1 *c.*1735–75, and much sought after

2 Mid- to late 18th century

3 Early 18th century

◁ **CHEST OF DRAWERS**
*A typical arrangement of
two short and three long
drawers is found below
the moulded overhanging
top of this simple chest. A
gentleman's clothes were
laid out and brushed on
the pull-out brushing
slide. The bracket feet are
original. 1775; 33in high.*
£2,500

▷ **GEORGE III SERPENTINE
CHEST** *There are four graduated
drawers and a brushing slide
below the eared top of this
mahogany chest. The canted
angles feature cluster columns.
On some such chests the top
drawer is fitted as a dressing
table. 1765; 33in high.*
£8,000–£12,000

◁ **AMERICAN KNEEHOLE
CHEST** *of a type seldom
produced outside Rhode
Island. This superb chest
in mahogany, ash and
tulipwood, with a typical
rounded block front and
stylized shell carving, is
attributed to the Townsend-
Goddard School in
Newport. Genuine
examples are extremely
rare and are valued at tens
of thousands of pounds.
1765–75; 34in high.*

▷ **TEAK MILITARY SECRETAIRE CHEST** *with drawer linings made of cedar. The top right-hand drawer front drops to form a writing surface, revealing several compartments for stationery and papers. Years of polishing have lent this piece an almost new look, but its construction dates it firmly to the second quarter of the 19th century. 1830; 3ft 3in high.* **£1,500**

CAMPAIGN CHESTS

First made in the late 18th century for officers on active service, the campaign, or military, chest came into vogue among the general public in the Regency and Victorian periods. Generally, it is these domestic campaign chests that have survived.

Most chests were made of teak or mahogany, with brass-bound corners, recessed handles and detachable feet for ease of transportation. As well as drawers, typical features included a mirror, wash basin and writing shelf.

◁ **WELLINGTON CHEST** *First made in the 19th century, such chests were named in the first Duke's honour. The left- and right-hand columns are hinged and lockable, and this burr walnut example would have been used to house coins, medals or specimens. 1845; 4ft high.* **£2,500**

OCCASIONAL
FURNITURE

The term "occasional furniture" covers
a broad range of relatively small pieces.
Much of this furniture, which includes
fire screens and wine coolers, was designed
for an occasional, specific, purpose and
was moved around as required. Many
pieces were made as "one-offs", not as part
of a larger set. Other occasional pieces,
such as miniature cabinets, were simply
smaller versions of existing furniture.
Growing numbers of nouveau riche artisans
and professionals from the mid-18th
century onward created a demand for the
styles of a grander age and class – but
condensed for smaller houses.
Occasional furniture is, therefore, ideally
suited to the modern interior and is
in great demand today. When intending
to buy, personal taste will count for much;
but the finest quality pieces are those
that are in original condition and display
good craftsmanship, attractive detailing
and the use of fine timbers.

SMALL LIBRARY FURNITURE

Until the 1730s, books were owned mainly by the rich, and the bookcases built to hold them, often designed as part of the architecture of a big room, were also large. Then, in the late 1700s, it became fashionable to collect paintings so, to make more wall space, bookcases became smaller and revolving bookcases were introduced.

At the same time, many types of reading chair were made. These included the "horseman's" chair, common in Georgian times,

on which the reader sat astride facing the back and rested his book on a stand attached to the top rail, and the upholstered armchair with a reading stand on one of the arms.

△ PAINTED REVOLVING BOOKSTAND *in an unusual mixture of West and East Indian satinwood. Such pieces, which were made from c.1890, copy those made 100 years earlier for drawing room use, but are smaller, and the painting is less sophisticated. c.1900; 4ft 10in high.* **£3,000**

▽ REVOLVING BOOKSTAND
An example of Edwardian Sheraton Revival style, decorated with stringing and crossbanding in a traditional manner. The three small drawers and cupboards make it a useful piece in a popular style. Early 1900s; 35in high. **£1,500**

◁ **MAHOGANY READING CHAIR** *with typical Regency splayed back legs and gadrooned front legs – features that became more marked as this type of chair continued to be made during the 1800s. The reading stand may have been replaced and the upholstery is not original. 1820–30; 3ft 4in high.* **£2,850**

▽ **BURR WALNUT WRITING SLOPE**
The cylindrical lid and inked-in walnut veneer of this writing slope are typically mid-Victorian. Original fittings include leather-covered tinder boxes with engraved metal lids, an inkwell, agate quill holder and gilt-metal paper knife. 1850s; 18in wide. **£650**

◁ **WRITING SLOPE** *in polished mahogany. Although military in style, with brass-reinforced corners and flush-fitting handles, this substantial box was intended for civilian use. It still contains the original brass-lidded inkwells. 1850s; 21in wide.* **£800**

Like bookcases, writing tables and desks were also large until the advent of the *bonheur du jour* (a small desk made for ladies' boudoirs) and the davenport. In Victorian times, the easily portable writing slope or writing box was popular.

A davenport is a small desk with a sliding or pull-out writing slope, to accommodate the knees, and drawers that open to the side. The first such desk was, according to tradition, ordered by a Captain Davenport in the late 1700s, and early examples were in a plain, military style.

By the 1820s, davenports had become fashionable, and

styles in rosewood, mahogany and, later, burr walnut veneer became ever more ornate. In the mid-1800s, demand outran the supply of high-class pieces, and many inferior models appeared. Almost every type of davenport had been made by the 1890s, and the vogue for them waned.

▷ **FINE CYLINDER FALL DAVENPORT**
veneered in burr walnut and decorated with marquetry panels. On top is a stationery box, and the cylinder top conceals a rising slope for writing, pen trays and drawers. Shelves to hold sheet music replace the usual drawers. 1865. **£2,500**

STYLES OF DAVENPORT

Early davenports were box shaped and fairly plain but, as designs changed, features such as scroll legs became common. Sometimes drawers

are hidden behind a door.
1 Scroll supports, flat top, 1865.
2 Scroll supports, piano-type top, 1865. **3** Turned supports, school desk type. 1840–85.

◁ **ROSEWOOD DAVENPORT** *with turned column supports in the Classical style and a bank of drawers for papers opening to the side. Around the top is a low brass gallery, and a small hinged drawer swings out to the side to hold the writer's pens and pencils. Early Victorian; 24in wide.* **£2,500**

▽ **BURR WALNUT DAVENPORT**
This ingeniously made piece has a counter-balanced rising top compartment for stationery and a writing surface which slides sideways to reveal a storage well. It is decorated throughout with split coloumn moulding, and the scrolling supports have fret-pierced panels. Mid-Victorian; 24in wide. **£3,500**

Miniature Cabinets

The portability of miniature cabinets means that examples from all over the world can be found in salerooms, and since they are often extremely decorative, these cabinets are popular with collectors.

Most miniature cabinets made in Europe are contemporary copies of full-sized pieces, not, as is often thought, prototypes for larger pieces. They are sometimes called "apprentice's pieces", because it is believed that such cabinets were often made by trainee cabinet makers to show that they were sufficiently skilled to set up on their own.

Early cabinets were used for storing anything from spices to candles, lace, ribbons, needlework and silks.

△ **CHINESE BLACK AND GILT LACQUER CABINET** *made for the export market. The design was copied from an early 18th-century cabinet. 1810; 20in high.*
£400–£600

▷ **JAPANESE PARQUETRY CABINET,** *with painted lacquer doors; the unique style and the view of Mount Fuji on the inside of the lid confirm its origin. Such mass-produced pieces tend to be inferior in quality. Late 1800s; 17in high.* **£100–£130**

△ **APOTHECARY'S CABINET** *made in rosewood with brass inlays and fitted with glass jars and bottles and two drawers. Its solid style reflects the status of the physician. 1820s; 15in high.* **£400–£600**

MINIATURE SPICE CABINET

Such cabinets, which began to appear in England at the end of the 1600s, were used for storing expensive exotic spices. They could be wall mounted or free standing, like this example in yew with a neat arrangement of drawers, each with its original gilt drop handle. *c.*1690; 19in high. **£3,500–£4,000**

DUMB WAITERS & WHATNOTS

The first dumb waiters appeared in the 1740s. The basic form is a central column on a tripod base, with three circular trays of graduated size. The name "dumb waiter" is derived from its function as a receptacle for food from which guests could help themselves.

Until the 1770s, decoration followed that of tripod tables. After that, distinct variations began to emerge, with the widest variety of styles produced in the Victorian period. Trays are most often dished, with a lip around the edge, but the finest are those with galleries.

In the late 18th century the plain whatnot first appeared. Initially used as a receptacle for books and manuscripts, it soon became a general "holdall". Victorian variations on the form included the whatnot "canterbury" (music stand) and the writing desk, with bookrests and drawers. Decoration took the form of pierced galleries, carved and turned spindles, deeply shaped shelving, and veneers and marquetry.

By the 1890s the vogue was for plainer, 18th-century-style "Revival" pieces, and the heyday of the whatnot passed.

◁▷ **GEORGIAN DUMB WAITERS** *It is unusual to find dumb waiters in pairs: in this fine mahogany example, the columns between the three dished trays are turned in a matching design. The use of dumb waiters protected indiscreet guests against possible blackmail by unscrupulous staff. 1785; 4ft 4in high.*
The pair **£15,000**

△ **WALNUT WHATNOT** *A highly ornate design with drawers in the base. Many whatnots were made of walnut, as well as painted beech and cheaper timbers such as pine and fruitwood, with the most expensive pieces exhibiting the finest craftsmanship. 1850s; 5ft 6in high.* **£1,500**

△ **WALNUT VENEERED WHATNOT** *with decorative boxwood inlays and a mirror. This piece is typical of mid-Victorian furniture made in the East End of London. 1860; 4ft 4in high.* **£500–£800**

CHANGING STYLES

Despite their different purposes, dumb waiters and whatnots are often confused. The problem was compounded in the 1800s, when rectangular and square trays became popular on dumb waiters as well as on whatnots.

LATE REGENCY
DUMB WAITER

GEORGE III
DUMB WAITER

19TH-CENTURY
DUMB WAITER

VICTORIAN
WHATNOT

VICTORIAN
CORNER
WHATNOT

WINE COOLERS & CELLARETS

The terms "wine cooler" and "cellaret" refer to items with distinct uses. A cellaret is a box for storing bottles and may have a lead or baize lining; a wine cooler keeps wine chilled during a meal.

Wine coolers were first used in England and in fine houses were made of silver. Georgian designs were similar but used marble or granite. After *c.*1730 mahogany exteriors with lead-lined interiors, filled with ice, were common. They rested on a stand or sideboard pedestal.

Cellarets stood on integral feet or legs and could be round, square or hexagonal in shape. By the 1760s many had separate containers for bottles and ice. As bottles became taller in the 18th century, so cellaret design changed to accommodate them.

△ **MAHOGANY WINE COOLER** *with decorative brass banding made in the time of George III. The interior is lead lined and a tap on the base allows the water to be drawn off as the ice melts. 1770; 26in high.* **£4,850**

△ **TRAVELLING CELLARET,** *or decanter box. This piece is in excellent condition, complete with original bottles, glasses and stoppers made of fine Dutch glass. Fragile details such as these, if damaged, would seriously affect the overall value. 1800; 16in high.* **£2,000**

WINE COOLER SHAPES

The tapering box and curvilinear styles were popular between 1750 and 1780. After that, rectangular pieces found favour, with the sarcophagus common from the late Regency onward.

A REGENCY CELLARET

This 22-inch-high mahogany cellaret, made in 1830, is valued at £1,200. The design of such boxes had changed little since the 1780s, but the bulbous turned legs and the moulding on the top of the stand are Regency features. In the late 19th century many cellarets were converted into boxes for needlework.

Internal divisions create spaces to accommodate six bottles.

◁ **LARGE WINE COOLER** *made in the Hepplewhite period with bands of decorative brasswork and cast brass side handles. The base, with four square, tapered legs and brass castors, is original, as is the lead lining of the interior. 1770; 28in high.* **£4,500**

TAPERING BOX 1760–80	CURVILINEAR 1750–80	RECTANGULAR 1780–1830	SARCOPHAGUS 1810 onward

FIRE SCREENS

Before the introduction of gas and electricity, fires were the major source of heat, consequently people sat close to them. It was not until the 18th century, however, that fire screens were widely used to shield the eyes from the glare when reading or doing needlework and to protect the face from the heat. This was particularly important, since wax was one of the main ingredients of cosmetics at the time.

Pole screens were generally made in pairs and consisted of a rectangular, shield-shaped or

▷ **ROSEWOOD POLE SCREEN** *This early Victorian piece, one of a pair, stands on a trefoil base and has a Berlin woolwork banner in a Rococo Revival shield-shaped frame. Although the original finial is missing, value is unaffected. 1835; 5ft high.* **The pair £1,500**

◁ **CHEVAL-TYPE SCREEN** *made in the 1920s by setting an 1845 sampler into an unadorned oak frame. Needlework panel screens date back to the early 1700s: a rectangular example attached to a wooden pole with a tripod base is illustrated in Chippendale's* Director *(1763). 1920; 28in high.* **£200–£300**

oval screen attached to a metal or wooden pole by a ring or screw, which allowed the height to be adjusted.

As well as pole screens for individual use, many 18th-century rooms had larger floor screens. These were known as "cheval" screens, from the French for horse, since they stood on four legs. A variation on the form was the fire screen desk, with a rectangular panel that pulled up at the rear. It was designed for use in the bedroom or smaller rooms of the house.

Fire screens were produced by leading cabinet makers of the period, such as Chippendale and Hepplewhite, while Ince and Mayhew sold mahogany-framed items with lacquer, silk or needlework decoration.

△ GEORGE III PANEL SCREEN
The English maker Thomas Chippendale supplied this mahogany fire screen. The canvas panels, depicting clematis and peonies, are of a later date. 1760–1830; 3ft 9in high. **£850**

FIRE SCREEN SHAPES

Adjustable pole screens from the mid-18th century typically display a simple elegance. In the Victorian period, shapes became more elaborate and opulent. With the increased use of gas for heat and light in the 19th century, pole screens became largely redundant. However, from the late 1800s onward larger cheval screens were favoured. The early 1900s saw the revival of popular Regency styles (see example from 1820).

1775   1780   1855

1820   1860

SMALL PINE FURNITURE

Pine, also known as deal, is a pale yellow to reddish softwood with a straight grain, which has long been used by European furniture makers. In areas where it was readily available, such as Scotland, Austria and Scandinavia, pine furniture was common; elsewhere, much of the pine was imported from the Baltic and later in the 1800s from North America.

City craftsmen employed pine mainly for drawer linings, backboards and carcasses that were later veneered in superior woods such as walnut. Country makers produced a wide variety

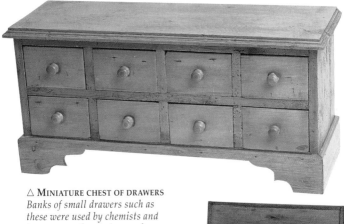

△ **MINIATURE CHEST OF DRAWERS**
Banks of small drawers such as these were used by chemists and ironmongers for storing goods; now they are bought mainly for use in the kitchen. When it was made, this piece was probably scumbled to resemble a more expensive wood. 1800; 30in wide. **£250**

◁△ **AUSTRIAN DEED OR BIBLE BOX**
with the original hand-forged iron strap hinges and fitted with an interior box for holding candles. The painted decoration, too, is original. 1840; 32in wide. **£300–£500**

of well-made pine furniture and other small domestic pieces.

Much country furniture was made by local carpenters and joiners using early construction methods, but in the 1800s, pine furniture was made both by hand and by machine in country styles. Handmade pieces are more expensive: they look less regular, the planks are generally wider, and the wood often has better colour and grain.

Although continental pine furniture and boxes were often painted, either in flat colours or with floral motifs, in Britain it was more usual for the wood to be scumbled. In this process, a piece of furniture was varnished and, while the varnish was still wet, the surface was combed or brushed into grain patterns similar to those of more desirable woods, such as mahogany and walnut.

▷ **STRIPPED BOW-FRONTED COMMODE,** *or chamber pot holder, with turned legs in the style popular at the time of William IV. A simulated mahogany grain pattern would almost certainly have been applied to this piece by a specialist workshop when it was made, but this finish has been removed. 1840; 29in high.* **£350–£400**

◁ **SUSSEX PANTRY TABLE** *The peg-jointed construction, short splayed legs and simple carving on the drawer front give this small piece a sturdy, unsophisticated air – a quality the Arts and Crafts Movement consciously strove to capture in their furniture later in the century. 1860s; 18in high.* **£400–£450**

CHILDREN'S FURNITURE

Apart from cradles and high chairs, children's furniture is really just a smaller model of adult furniture. It is generally of good quality since most of what survives today was commissioned by wealthy parents. The richer the family, the more faithful and elaborate the piece.

▽ **MAHOGANY CRADLE** *The design of this fine quality cradle is copied from oak cradles made in the late 1600s and early 1700s. The true date of the piece is, however, given away by the wood used and by the stylized sunflower on the back, a motif favoured in late Victorian times. 1885; 3ft 2in long.* **£500**

STYLES OF CRADLE

The best early cradles were made of oak; later examples were constructed of mahogany, cane and even wrought iron. Cradle styles developed from the simple carved box on rockers to the more sophisticated boat shape on a swing frame which kept the baby off the ground.

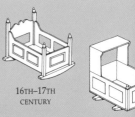

16TH–17TH
CENTURY

17TH–EARL
18TH CENTU

Even famous makers, such as Thomas Chippendale, made furniture for the children of their most important clients.

Most children's furniture was a small-scale version of the adult piece. It should not be confused with dolls' furniture or traveller's samples, which tend to be too small for use.

Chairs are the most common pieces of child's furniture found today. They were first recorded in Elizabethan times, when they were similar to those of adults, but had longer legs.

◁ **OAK HIGH CHAIR** *Made during the reign of Charles II, this piece would originally have had finials on its top. It is very similar to the type of chair the child's parents would have used, albeit with longer legs. It has a carved back panel, scrolled arms and turned legs joined by square stretchers. 1660–85; 32in high.* **£4,000**

▽ **BENTWOOD ARMCHAIR** *This type of chair, invented by the Austrian Michael Thonet, derives its name from the way the frame was bent using steam. Popular since the 1830s, millions were made. This child's version still has its maker's label. 1890; 27in high.* **£125–£175**

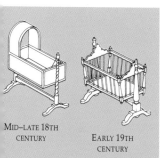

MID–LATE 18TH CENTURY

EARLY 19TH CENTURY

In the 18th century, children's chairs imitated the sophisticated curvilinear lines of the adult Queen Anne pieces. As with earlier children's chairs, the legs were extra long. During this century a new type of miniature chair developed. It stood on a movable platform which could double as a child's table. This design was the forerunner of the high chair and could, by 1800, be attached by means of a coach bolt to the edge of a table.

Cane was first imported for use in chair making in the time of Charles II. It was split and woven to produce seats and chair backs not only for adult chairs but also for the miniature

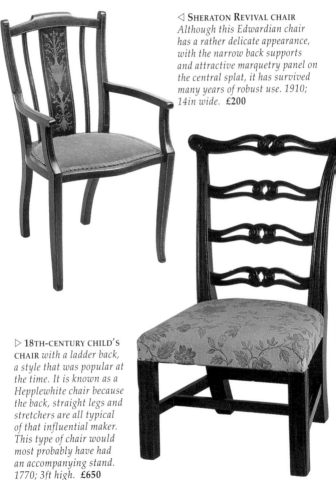

◁ **SHERATON REVIVAL CHAIR**
Although this Edwardian chair has a rather delicate appearance, with the narrow back supports and attractive marquetry panel on the central splat, it has survived many years of robust use. 1910; 14in wide. **£200**

▷ **18TH-CENTURY CHILD'S CHAIR** *with a ladder back, a style that was popular at the time. It is known as a Hepplewhite chair because the back, straight legs and stretchers are all typical of that influential maker. This type of chair would most probably have had an accompanying stand. 1770; 3ft high.* **£650**

versions used by children. These
diminutive models had the
added charm of baluster- or
bobbin-pattern turned uprights
that were out of proportion to
the rest of the chair.

As time progressed children's
furniture continued to be made
in a huge variety of styles
reflecting the prevailing fashion.

▷ CHILD'S WINDSOR CHAIR
*The turned leg and arm supports
and the pierced splat on this fine
hoopback chair are exact replicas
of those found on the full-size
chairs. It was constructed using
two woods: yew and beech.
1850; 3ft 4in high.* **£650**

PAPIER MÂCHÉ CHAIR

Made from layers of paper
pulp moulded and pressed
into shape, papier mâché
originated in the East. In
Victorian times, it became
very fashionable to make
small furniture, such as this
chair, by moulding papier
mâché on a metal or
wooden frame.

The original seat of this
early Victorian chair would
have been made of cane.

When the present seat was put
on, in the early 1900s, it was
painted to match the attractive
Japanese-style decoration on
the back. *c.*1840; 17in high. **£185**

CARING FOR YOUR VALUABLES

ANTIQUES MAY BE BOUGHT FOR THEIR beauty, craftsmanship, history, rarity or even for their curiosity value. It does not matter whether you buy an item because it gives you pleasure, or because you consider it to be a serious investment: it is important to see that it is well looked after and properly insured. That way, it can be enjoyed today and handed down from generation to generation.

Owning a piece of antique furniture is, however, only half the story. Precious pieces also require care and, often, repair. But bear in mind that if you are planning to sell a piece, it may be better to leave it in its original condition, since collectors sometimes prefer to have any repair work carried out themselves.

In almost all instances, it is unwise to try to restore furniture yourself. Poor-quality repairs will often considerably reduce a piece's value; more importantly, they can cause irreversible damage. Experts always advise owners to seek out a first-class repairer or restorer. Even if their charges are fairly high, it is cost effective to pay the price for excellent work.

After you have used furniture for many years, it is wise to have it checked over by a skilled repairer and to have loose joints or flaking veneers fixed – before you pass it on to your heirs!

CARING FOR FURNITURE

1 The most important thing about looking after antique furniture is to remember that "gently does it". It is very easy to remove patina and colour but impossible to replace them. Light dusting with a soft cloth and occasional cleaning and polishing are all that is needed.

2 The safest way to clean antique furniture is to apply a little clear wax with a soft shoe brush, rub vigorously, then buff it with a soft cloth. If any more cleaning is needed, consult an expert. Good-quality furniture will already have been treated with grain filler and surface polish, so little further attention is required.

3 Never strip the surface of a piece of furniture. For instance, with some wax polishes the instructions for use recommend application with wire wool. Never do this: the combination of wax and wire wool will undo the patina that has been acquired over generations in two or three strokes.

4 Don't use "traditional" remedies, such as lemon juice, olive oil or methylated spirit, and avoid patent cleaning mixtures.

5 If stains have been made by plant pots, flower vases or glasses, do not apply anything to the mark until it is properly dry – at least two weeks. It is worth being patient because in most instances the black stain will disappear of its own accord. The application of any "remedy" may mean that the scar becomes permanent.

6 Wooden furniture should not stand in direct sunlight; prolonged exposure will bleach out the colour. Neither should it be placed close to any source of heat, such as a central heating radiator, hot air duct, electric or open fire. This will cause the wood to dry out and crack, veneers and inlays to shrink and warp and joints to open up. Keep the air moist by standing a bowl of water near the heat source or by installing a humidifier.

7 Don't polish gilded or brass handles. If the gilding has worn away, the handle underneath should appear bronze coloured.

8 Ormolu mounts should be dusted gently with a soft brush but should never be polished, even with a dry cloth. Never have faded ormolu regilded; this may detract from the value of the piece.

9 Take expert advice before changing upholstery. Reupholstery should be carried out using traditional materials, such as canvas webbing and horsehair

padding, not foam rubber. Fabric should be secured with tacks, not a staple gun.

10 Upholstered furniture can be carefully vacuumed; secure a cloth over the nozzle of the vacuum cleaner if the upholstery is worn.

11 Make sure that the seat is returned to its original chair when drop-in seats are reupholstered. The shape of seats varies marginally and the incorrect seat can put a strain on chair joints.

12 Leave the repair of chipped gilding to the expert. Chips can be filled and painted to match, but this is not a job for the amateur.

13 Furniture should be inspected at least twice a year for woodworm infestation, and if tiny holes and fresh sawdust are found, the piece should be treated with woodworm fluid.

INSURANCE

The question of insurance is a matter of personal choice, and insurance companies vary greatly in the types of cover they provide – and the cost of the premiums. Cover for very valuable antiques can be expensive, but trying to find the lowest quotation is not necessarily the wisest course. Specialist brokers, as well as building society insurance services, understand the needs of collectors.

The first thing to do is to decide on the nature of the cover

you require: the kind of "risks". Comprehensive and All In policies cover only certain specified perils, such as theft, fire, explosion, water damage or storm damage. In the event of theft, evidence will be required before a claim is met, and insurance companies will ask if the police have been notified.

Another type of cover is All Risks, which represents the maximum cover you are likely to obtain. It will also cover you against accidental breakage and disappearance, but not "inherent vice", such as the progressive deterioration of upholstery fabrics through atmospheric conditions.

Decide exactly what you want to insure and list the items with as much detail as possible. If your collection consists of a number of small items, such as tea caddies, you may need to list them all. It is advisable to keep receipts as back-up evidence if you have to make a claim. Insurance companies also sometimes ask to see photographs, credit card vouchers or notes of any distinguishing marks on the pieces of furniture.

You may even need to consider a policy that covers your possessions away from home, for example when they are sent to restorers or if you are selling them at an antiques fair.

VALUING YOUR POSSESSIONS

If you want to get a valuation of items you have inherited or had for some time, it is usually a good idea to obtain two quotes: from either reputable dealers or auction houses. (You may have to pay them a small percentage of the value.)

Most insurance valuations are based on the full market price, or replacement cost, of an item. That is why it is important to give your insurers as much detail as possible. For example, where the furniture is kept and how it is protected. If you underinsure, insurance companies are likely to scale down their pay-outs – or may even refuse to pay out at all. It is now fairly standard practice for an insurer not to pay a claim in cash, but to settle the claim once you have bought a replacement. Frequently you are expected to pay an "excess", which can be, for example, the first £25 of the cost of each claim.

Index-linked policies automatically adjust the amount of insurance cover, and your premiums, every year. But it is still worth checking the figures from time to time. It is a good idea to have valuations updated every few years because fantastic appreciation often occurs with certain periods or pieces.

LOOKING AFTER YOUR ANTIQUES

Insurers are very keen that you take "reasonable" care of valuable items. Keep furniture at an even temperature in a dry place and away from a source of direct heat. Don't keep valuable pieces under a water tank or bathroom.

It also makes sense to install smoke detectors, particularly in living areas, and to have fire extinguishers easily to hand.

If something does get broken or damaged, get the written approval of your insurance company before having it restored.

SECURITY

According to research, 1 in 12 households is burgled annually. But by joining a Neighbourhood Watch scheme, not only can the risk be reduced to 1 in 75, but you could also lower the cost of your home contents premium. The local Crime Prevention Officer will be happy to help you set up a scheme if none exists. Usually you need half the people in your area – whether it is a street or block of flats – to agree to join.

Normally your Crime Prevention Officer will also be happy to advise you if the locks and bolts on your property are adequate. Security devices such as five-lever mortise locks on doors and key-operated window locks are fairly inexpensive to fit and highly effective; they may even help to reduce the cost of your premiums.

As a rule, two mortise dead-locks should be fitted to each external door, and window locks to all ground-floor and first-floor windows. Vulnerable windows, such as those in a basement, should be fitted with iron bars. Additional precautions, such as security bolts on doors, are worth considering, especially where a door is not made of timber or is less than 1¾ inches thick.

Alarms are another way of deterring burglars, and they can also reduce your premiums. Don't go for the cheapest quote just to save a few pounds: choose a recognized organization that offers local maintenance facilities and a full guarantee. The local police or your insurers will probably be able to recommend appropriate companies to you.

If your home does get burgled, you should report the matter at the police station and to your insurers without delay.

National & Provincial Building Society, whose support helped to make this book possible, offers the insurance services the collector requires. Advice is available from its branches, or call the Freefone advice line on 0800 80 80 80.

COLLECTOR'S CHECKLIST

PROBABLY THE MOST ENJOYABLE aspect of collecting antique furniture is that every piece is a tangible item of history – part of the society of an earlier period.

You should not be afraid of antique furniture. Just as a house needs to be lived in, so furniture needs to be used. A family dining table made in 1760, for instance, should still be enjoyed. With care and normal use, it has lasted until today, and with the same treatment it should continue to offer good service for another 200 years or so.

Encourage children to use, and respect, antique furniture, for in this way they will grow to enjoy our heritage.

There is no real mystique to antique furniture: understanding it is merely a logical process, but with experience and appreciation of manufacturing techniques and design styles comes deeper knowledge.

When you look at a piece, mentally check that its use, the material it is made from, its shape and decoration had all been "invented" at the time the piece was supposed to have been made.

For example, there will be no Elizabethan satinwood teapoys with Classical decoration. First, tea was not known in the West; second, satinwood was not used for furniture; and, third, cabinet makers knew little of Classical decoration.

Antique furniture in perfect condition is usually prohibitively expensive, but many collectors buy pieces in need of restoration. However, it is important to check that a piece is worth restoring. It should be missing few elements (brass inlay or ormolu mounts can be extremely expensive to replace) and to merit restoration the wood should be of fine quality and not too badly warped, since the work of professional cabinet makers does not come cheap.

The method of construction will help to establish the date at which furniture was made. From the end of the 15th century until well into the 17th, most joints on chairs and other furniture were of the mortise and tenon type. Until c.1700, two large dovetail joints were used where the end grain of wood was joined to the side grain (as with drawer corners); after that date, dovetails became more numerous and more precise.

Styles of handles, locks, castors, screws and hinges, and the materials from which they were made, can all be dated to a greater or lesser extent, and all help to establish authenticity.

The style of the feet and legs on a piece of furniture can be another good indication of period. Even styles that were reproduced at a later date have subtle differences which allow them to be distinguished from the original. For instance, 18th-century cabriole legs were usually more finely carved than those on later reproductions, which took a more exaggerated form.

"Earpieces" at the top of cabriole legs were always made separately and glued on. Replacements can be spotted by comparing the colour and carving with the rest of the leg.

TIPS FOR BUYERS

1 Look carefully at the colour of the wood. On an exposed surface it will be fresh and dry. In hidden areas it will be darker, but still dry. The build-up of grease and wax, naturally leading to a mellow colour, is termed patina and is almost impossible to fake.

Patina does not build up evenly; in places such as the top rail of a dining chair, or the overhang of a fold-over table, where hands have held or lifted it, oils from the skin will have helped to created a good patina, slightly darkening the wood. It takes many years for a good patina to develop.

2 Chests of drawers have often had several sets of handles. The way to detect this is to check inside the drawer fronts for holes which may have been filled and disguised. A layer of dirt and grease will have accumulated around handles that have been on a piece for a long time, and they may have marked the front of the drawer where they have knocked against it.

3 Deep 18th-century chests of drawers have often been made narrower. Take out a drawer and check that the grooves for the drawer runners stop short of the backboard and that the dovetails on drawers are all of the same quality.

4 Victorian bow-fronted chests vary little from those of the 18th century in basic structure, but details such as a heavy overhanging top and bulky feet can be a guide. Check closely for disguises in both places.

5 Table tops are often married to legs that do not belong to them; for instance, small tripod tables are sometimes made up with legs taken from a fire screen. Where the pedestal meets the underside of a tilt-top table, the marks on both parts should correspond.

6 The underside of the top of a gate-leg table should show the marks caused by the legs being pulled out and where the top has rested.

7 Table edges should show the signs of many years use; too perfect an edge suggests that the top may have been cut down or heavily restored.

8 Check that areas of wear on the top rails and stretchers of chairs are genuine and that they have not been artificially "distressed". Wear should show mainly on the front stretcher, where feet have been placed.

9 The feet on furniture can be a useful indicator of period, although there may be pitfalls, since, like handles, they were sometimes altered to reflect the prevailing fashion or to replace worn original feet. Replacement feet do not necessarily detract from a piece unless they are out of style.

10 Original carving always stands proud of the outline of a piece; it is never recessed. In the same way, 18th-century beading was carved from wood left on a piece of furniture for that purpose, so the grain pattern will be true; by contrast, Victorian beading was carved separately and then glued in place.

GLOSSARY

Note: SMALL CAPITALS within an entry refer to another entry.

A

AESTHETIC MOVEMENT Decorative arts movement, greatly influenced by Oriental styles, that flourished in North America and Britain *c.*1870–80.

APRON Shaped wooden edging that hangs below a drawer line or table top.

ARTS AND CRAFTS MOVEMENT Started in the late 1800s in Britain by a group of artists and craftsmen committed to handmade, not machine-made, articles.

B

BACKBOARD The unpolished back of a piece of furniture, not meant to be seen.

BACKPLATE Plate behind a handle.

BACK STOOL A stool with a back which later evolved into the side chair.

BALLOON-BACK CHAIR Chair with a round or oval-shaped back and nipped waist, popular *c.*1820–1900.

BALUSTER Turned column with a curving shape, used for table legs and chair backs.

BANDING Decorative strips of INLAY or VENEER. Straight banding is cut with the grain; crossbanding is cut across it.

BAROQUE Ornate 17th-C Italian style of architecture which influenced the decorative arts *c.*1660–1730.

BENTWOOD Lightweight or laminated timbers that are bent into curves by steaming or soaking in hot water.

BERLIN WOOLWORK Wool needlework depicting pastoral scenes, flowers or landscapes. Popular in Victorian times.

BLOCK FRONT Front of a piece of furniture with two outward curves on either side of a central inward curve; common on American pieces.

BOBBIN TURNING Decoration, found on 17th- and 18th-C chair and table legs and STRETCHERS, consisting of a series of wooden spheres turned on a lathe.

BOW FRONT Curving, convex front on furniture such as chests of drawers.

BRACKET FOOT Squared foot, generally used on 18th-C cabinet furniture.

BURR WALNUT Wood cut from a cross-section of a gall or from the gnarled grain at the base of a tree; often used for VENEERS.

C

CABRIOLE Leg with a double curve: outward at the knee and inward above the foot.

CARCASS Main body of a piece of furniture, excluding doors and drawers.

CASE FURNITURE A piece of furniture, such as a chest of drawers, made to contain something.

CHIP CARVING Pattern cut out of a wooden panel by chipping.

CHIPPENDALE, THOMAS (1718–79) English cabinet maker and designer, very influential in the mid-GEORGIAN period in England and the U.S.

CLASSICAL STYLE 18th-C style much influenced by the arts and culture of ancient Greece and Rome.

CLAW AND BALL Foot shaped like a ball gripped by a claw. Used from *c.*1720, often together with the CABRIOLE leg.

COCKBEADING Beaded moulding projecting from the surface; often used on drawer fronts.

CYLINDER TOP Slatted or ridged curved lid that slides down from inside the top of a desk to cover the desktop.

D, E

DOVETAIL Close-fitting joint with interlocking tenons. Used for drawers.

EBONIZED WOOD Wood stained and polished to look like ebony.

ESCUTCHEON Decorative metal plate surrounding a keyhole.

F

FINIAL Carved, turned or metal ornament on the top of a piece of furniture.

FRET PIERCING Fine decoration made by piercing the wood with a fret saw.

FRIEZE DRAWER Drawer in the frieze, or framework, just below a table top.

G

GADROONING Carved or moulded border made up of a series of convex curves.

GALLERY Border around the top edge of a piece of furniture.

GEORGIAN British style roughly covering the reigns of George I (1714–27) to George III (1760–1820).

GOTHIC Style that flourished in medieval times and was revived in the 18th C and 19th C. Pointed arches with slender lines and pierced tracery are typical.

H

HEPPLEWHITE, GEORGE (d.1786) English cabinet maker and furniture designer. An exponent of the NEO-CLASSICAL style, his designs are typified by their utility, elegance and simplicity.

HOOPBACK CHAIR Chair whose top rail and uprights form a continuous curve.

I

INCE AND MAYHEW Important English furniture makers of the mid-18th C.

INLAY Decorative technique in which woods, metal, ivory or mother-of-pearl are set into recesses cut in the surface of a piece of furniture.

L, M

LACQUER Hard glossy resin from the tree *Rhus vernicifera* built up in several layers on a piece and then carved or inlaid with various materials.

LADDERBACK CHAIR Chair with horizontal rails or slats, giving the appearance of a ladder.

LOWBOY Small side table on CABRIOLE legs.

MARQUETRY Design formed from VENEERS of different coloured woods.

N, O

NEO-CLASSICISM Style popular in the late 18th C, using motifs inspired by the art and architecture of the CLASSICAL civilizations in a different context.

OGEE Double curve, convex at the top and becoming concave at the bottom.

ORMOLU The term was used originally for the powdered gold used to gild furniture mounts made from bronze and other metals. Now it is used for the mounts themselves.

OYSTER VENEER Type of VENEER made from vertical sections cut from the branches of walnut or laburnum trees, whose pattern resembles an oyster.

P

PAD FOOT Simple terminal to a CABRIOLE leg, resting on a small disc, or pad.

PAPIER MÂCHÉ Paper pulp moulded to make small items; it is often LACQUERED.

PARQUETRY Form of VENEER, usually laburnum "oysters", whose pattern is geometric.

R

REGENCY British decorative style named after the Prince Regent who ruled in the place of George III from 1811 to 1820 and as George IV until 1830.

ROCOCO Elaborate curvilinear style that originated in France in the 18th C.

RUNNERS Strips of wood on which drawers slide.

S

SABRE LEG Sharply curved leg in the CLASSICAL style.

SEAT RAIL Horizontal frame just below the seat of a chair that joins the chair legs.

SERPENTINE FRONT Sinuous double-curved front found on chest furniture, especially in the 18th C.

SHERATON, THOMAS (1751–1806) English designer whose light, delicate furniture expressed the NEO-CLASSICAL style.

SHIELD BACK Design of chair back often used by HEPPLEWHITE in the 1780s.

SPLAT Central upright of a wooden chair back, rising from the seat to the top rail.

STRETCHER Horizontal strut or rail bracing the legs of a chair or table.

STRINGING INLAY consisting of fine lines of metal or contrasting wood.

U, V

URN TABLE Small 18th-C table designed to hold a water urn or kettle.

VENEER Thin sheet of attractively grained wood (often walnut, satinwood or rosewood) applied to a surface.

INDEX